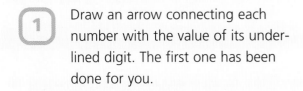

D1586800

The Value of Numbers

① Draw an arrow connecting each number with the value of its underlined digit. The first one has been done for you.

137   3 units
203   3 hundreds
3417   3 tens
4329   3 tenths
26.35   3 thousands
18.13   3 hundredths

② Paul has these four number cards:

He can use them to make the 3-digit number

a) What is the largest 2-digit number he can make with these cards?

b) What is the smallest 3-digit number he can make with these cards?

c) What is the largest 4-digit number he can make with these cards?

d) What is the smallest 4-digit number he can make with these cards?

e) If Paul had one more card with a number between 1 and 9 on, what would be the largest number he could make?

③ **a)** What is the largest 4-digit number you can make if all the digits are different?

b) What is the smallest 4-digit number you can make, if you are allowed to put a decimal point in, and if all the digits are different?

④ Bryony has these four different number cards:

a) Use these cards to make a number between 1750 and 2000.

b) Make a number between 6500 and 7500.

⑤ Charles has the same number cards as Bryony, but he also has 2 zeros and a decimal point.

a) What is the smallest number he could make?

b) What is the largest number he could make?

c) Use all 7 cards to make a number between 1000 and 1100.

Reading and Writing Numbers

1 Write these numbers in words.

a) 410

b) 2008

c) 5107

d) 12030

2 Write these numbers in figures.

a) Five hundred and four

b) Seven thousand and sixty

c) Three thousand eight hundred

d) Fifteen thousand and twelve

3 Write these Globalot lottery jackpots in figures.

a) Two million pounds

b) One million, six hundred thousand pounds

c) Seven million, one hundred and five thousand pounds

d) Eleven million, eleven thousand and eleven pounds

4 Write these Globalot lottery jackpots in words.

GLOBALOT
JACKPOT
12 MILLION

a) £1 500 000

b) £408 000

c) £1 201 201

d) £3.4 million

e) £2.75 million

Ordering Numbers

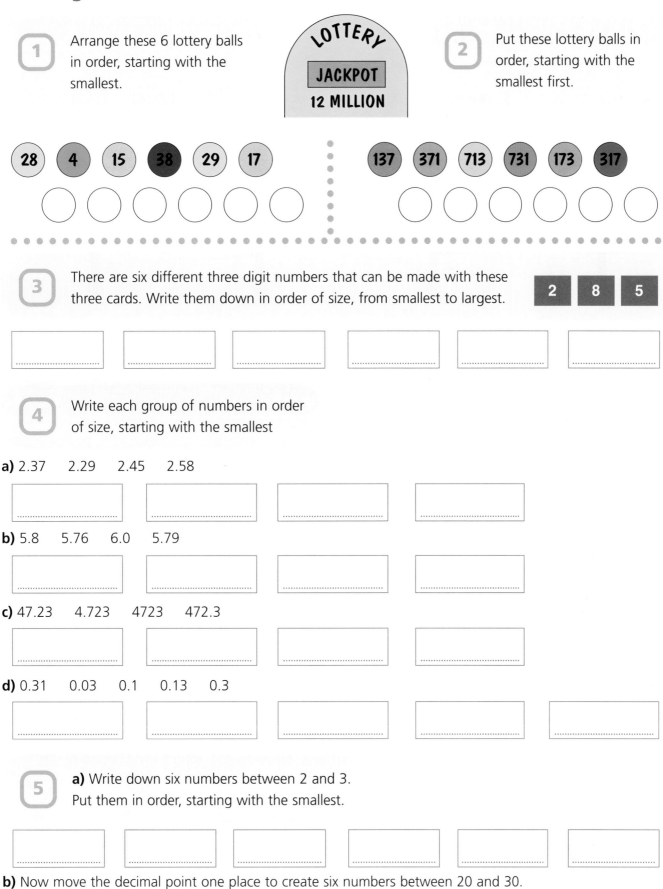

1 Arrange these 6 lottery balls in order, starting with the smallest.

LOTTERY
JACKPOT
12 MILLION

2 Put these lottery balls in order, starting with the smallest first.

28 4 15 38 29 17

137 371 713 731 173 317

3 There are six different three digit numbers that can be made with these three cards. Write them down in order of size, from smallest to largest.

2 8 5

4 Write each group of numbers in order of size, starting with the smallest

a) 2.37   2.29   2.45   2.58

b) 5.8   5.76   6.0   5.79

c) 47.23   4.723   4723   472.3

d) 0.31   0.03   0.1   0.13   0.3

5 **a)** Write down six numbers between 2 and 3.
Put them in order, starting with the smallest.

b) Now move the decimal point one place to create six numbers between 20 and 30.

Negative Numbers

1 Write down the temperatures on these thermometers.

a)
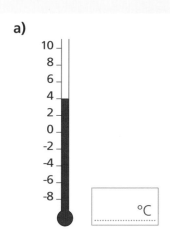
°C

b)
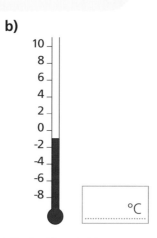
°C

c)
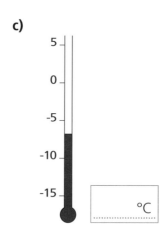
°C

d)
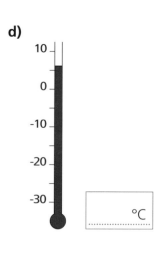
°C

2 Write these temperatures in order, starting with the coldest.

a) -1°C   0.5°C   -2°C   5°C   -3.2°C

b) -11°C   -13°C   -8°C   -2°C   -9°C

3 Mark the position of each of these numbers on the number line.

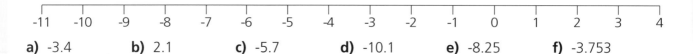

a) -3.4   **b)** 2.1   **c)** -5.7   **d)** -10.1   **e)** -8.25   **f)** -3.753

4 Use less than < or greater than > signs to make these statements correct. The first one has been done for you.

a) -1 > -3

b) -1 ☐ 3

c) 5 ☐ 2

d) -3 ☐ 2

e) 7.25 ☐ 7.3

f) 2.3 ☐ 2.19

g) 1010 ☐ 1101

h) -2.3 ☐ -2.29

5 Write down the smallest whole number that could go in these boxes.

a) 13 + ☐ > 15

b) 21 - ☐ > 18

c) 14 < ☐ + 9

d) 140 + ☐ >150

e) 363 - ☐ < 360

f) 110<104 + ☐

g) 450 < ☐ - 38

h) 47 - ☐ < 24

Multiplying and Dividing by 10 and 100

YOU MUST NOT USE A CALCULATOR

① Draw an arrow connecting each calculation with its answer. The first one has been done for you.

350 x 1000   3500
350 ÷ 10   35
35 x 100   350
35 x 10   35000
3500 ÷ 100

② Put a circle around the number which is 805 x 10.

850   8050   8500   8005   815

③ Write in the missing numbers.

a) ☐ x 10 = 6300

b) 15 x 10 = ☐

c) ☐ ÷ 10 = 82

d) 6030 ÷ ☐ = 603

e) ☐ x 100 = 2400

f) 18 x ☐ = 1800

g) ☐ ÷ 100 = 50

h) 36000 ÷ 10 = ☐

i) 2500 x 10 = ☐

j) 50100 ÷ ☐ = 501

④ Write what the four missing digits could be.

a) ☐☐☐ ÷ 10 = | 6 | ☐ |

b) ☐ | 1 | x 10 = ☐☐☐

c) ☐☐ x 10 = | 4 | ☐☐

d) ☐☐ x 100 = ☐ | 2 | 0 | ☐

⑤ Year 6 are holding a sponsored relay race around a 100m track.

a) What is the total distance covered after 8 laps?

_____ m

b) What is the total distance covered after 33 laps?

_____ m

c) How many laps did they complete if they covered a total distance of 5200m? ☐

⑥ Chocco bars are sold in packs of 10. *CHOCCO*

a) How many bars are there in 7 packs?

_____

b) How many bars are there in 150 packs?

_____

c) How many packs are needed for 1000 bars?

_____

Multiplying and Dividing by 10, 100 and 1000

YOU MUST NOT USE A CALCULATOR

1 Complete these sentences.

a) When you multiply by 1000, the digits move

[ ] places to the left.

b) When you divide by 100, the digits move

[ ] places to the [ ]

c) When you multiply by 10, the digits move

[ ] place to the [ ]

2 Put a circle around the number which is 3.5 x 10.

3.50   3.05   0.35   35   350

3 Put a circle around the number which is 87 x 1000.

87000   8700   8007   8070   80700

4 Peter has these "operation cards":

| x 10 | x 100 | x 1000 |

| ÷ 10 | ÷ 100 | ÷ 1000 |

Choose the card which makes the calculations correct.

a) 36 [ ] = 3.6   **b)** 45 [ ] = 4500

c) 2700 [ ] = 2.7   **d)** 817 [ ] = 81.7

e) 0.99 [ ] = 990   **f)** 860 [ ] = 8.60

g) 13.25 [ ] = 132.5   **h)** 36.1 [ ] = 3.61

5 Selina and Gemma were taking part in a swimathon. The swimming pool is 21m long.

a) How far had Selina swam after she had completed 10 lengths?

b) They swam a total of 100 lengths between them. How far did Selina and Gemma swim altogether?

c) To change m into km you need to divide by 1000. How many km did Selina and Gemma swim altogether?

Adding and Subtracting

1 Each side of these squares must add up to 20. Write in the missing numbers.

a)

5	8	
		6
9	4	

b)

	3	
7		5
	9	

2 Find the answers to these adding chains.

a) (1) + (2) + (3) + (4) + (5)

= [ ]

b) (3) + (4) + (5) + (6) + (7)

= [ ]

3 Fill in the missing numbers.

a) 8 + 9 = [ ]

b) 7 + [ ] = 11

c) 19 - [ ] = 7

d) [ ] - 12 = 8

e) 12 - 8 = [ ]

f) [ ] + 13 = 19

g) 20 - [ ] = 4

h) 17 - 8 = [ ]

i) [ ] + 6 = 28

j) 17 + [ ] = 35

4 Put rings around the two numbers which have a difference of 7.

8   11   17   6   21   19   13   5

5 Use these number cards to get the correct answers.

| 7 | 14 | 20 |
| 4 | 5 | 13 |

a) [ ] + [ ] + [ ] = 16

b) [ ] - [ ] = [ ]

c) [ ] + [ ] - [ ] = 14

d) [ ] + 8 = [ ] + [ ] + [ ]

6 Fill in the missing numbers so that each side of these triangles adds up to 18.

a)

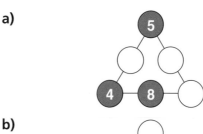

b)

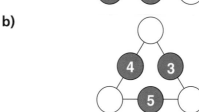

c)

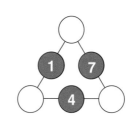

Adding and Subtracting - By Other Means

1 Use near doubles to help you answer these questions.

a) 36 + 37 =

b) 27 + 29 =

c) 180 + 180 =

d) 270 + 280 =

e) 2.5 + 2.6 =

f) 413 + 392 =

2 Try counting on or back in tens or hundreds to do these.

a) 231 + 80 =

b) 315 - 70 =

c) 640 + 600 =

d) 1240 - 700 =

e) 12311 + 8000 =

f) 36400 - 9000 =

3 Answer these - try and think of different ways of doing them.

a) 116 + 79 =

b) 234 - 88 =

c) 2140 + 488 =

d) 6.4 + 2.9 =

e) 18.1 - 1.9 =

f) 12.4 - 3.1 =

4 Here are some more.

a) 276 + 94 =

b) 274 - 96 =

c) 3006 - 1994 =

d) 5992 + 6012 =

e) 3.19 + 2.86 =

f) 8.1 - 2.9 =

5 Stacey has these cards:

| 49 | 112 | 63 | + | – | = |

She uses them to make this calculation:

| 49 | + | 63 | = | 112 |

Use the cards to complete these calculations correctly.

a) [   ] - 49 = [   ]

b) [   ] [   ] [   ] = 49

Adding and Subtracting - Written Methods

YOU MUST NOT USE A CALCULATOR

1 Write in the missing digits

a)

```
    5  [ ]  7
 +  [ ]  9  [ ]
 ─────────────
    7  6  5
```

b)

```
    7  4  5
 -  2  [ ]  7
 ─────────────
   [ ]  9  [ ]
```

c)

```
   [ ]  6 . [ ]
 +  1  [ ] . 9
 ─────────────
    7  4 . 3
```

d)

```
       3 . [ ]
 -  [ ] . 9  [ ]
 ─────────────
    1 . 6  4
```

2 The following cards can be used to make the sum: 568 + 790 = 1358

| 5 | 6 | 7 | 8 | 9 | 0 |

a) What is the biggest sum that can be made using these cards?

b) The cards can also be used to make two 3-digit numbers with a difference of 229
e.g. 789 - 560 = 229. Use the cards to make two 3-digit numbers with a difference of 281.

[ ] [ ] [ ] − [ ] [ ] [ ] = 281

c) What is the biggest difference between two 3-digit numbers that can be found using these cards?

3 Here are six cards.

| 47.8 | 23.6 | 81.2 | 63.9 | 17.0 | 50.4 |

a) Which two cards have a sum of 98.2?

[ ] + [ ] = 98.2

b) Which two cards have a difference of 17.3?

[ ] − [ ] = 17.3

c) Which three cards have a sum of 135.3?

[ ] + [ ] + [ ] = 135.3

d) Complete the following sum.

[ ] − [ ] − [ ] = 40.6

Multiplying and Dividing

1 Agent Muldoon has a secret code.

a	b	c	d	e	f	g	h	i	j	k	l	m	n	o	p	q	r	s	t	u	v	w	x	y	z
9	12	14	15	16	18	20	21	24	25	27	28	30	32	35	36	40	42	45	48	49	54	56	63	64	72

Decode this message.
The first letter has been done for you.

6 x 4 = 24   i

8 x 6 =

5 x 9 =

9 x 4 =

3 x 3 =

6 x 7 =

6 x 8 =

8 x 8 =

8 x 6 =

3 x 8 =

6 x 5 =

4 x 4 =

2 Find the cost of these sweets:

 7p EACH Chocolate Mice

 8p EACH Shoe Laces

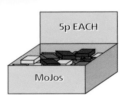 5p EACH MoJos

 4p EACH Cherry Lips

 6p EACH Jelly Beans

a) 5 chocolate mice ____ p
b) 6 shoe laces ____ p
c) 9 mojos ____ p

d) 8 cherry lips ____ p
e) 7 jelly beans ____ p
f) 7 chocolate mice ____ p

g) i) How many shoe laces can be bought with 50p ____ and **ii)** with 75p? ____

h) i) How many cherry lips can be bought with 30p ____ and **ii)** with £1? ____

3 In these shapes, the number in each square is found by multiplying the numbers in the circles on either side. Fill in the missing numbers.

a)
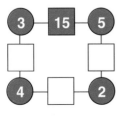

b)
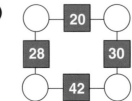

c)
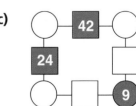

Multiplying and Dividing - Some Useful Methods

YOU MUST NOT USE A CALCULATOR

1 Mrs. Roberts wants to buy some prizes for her class.

a) Find the cost of 4 Chocco bars.

b) Find the cost of 8 cans of Cola.

2 Mrs. Gill divides a packet of 132 mints equally between her four children. How many mints does each child get?

3 **a)** A farmer has 83 cows, how many legs do they have altogether?

b) His neighbour's cows have 316 legs altogether. How many cows has he got?

4 Use repeated doubling to answer the following:

a) 14 x 4 =

b) 14 x 8 =

c) 28 x 8 =

d) 24 x 4 =

e) 24 x 8 =

f) 24 x 12 =

5 Work out these multiplications:

a) 7 x 19 =

b) 7 x 29 =

c) 7 x 79 =

d) 15 x 19 =

e) 15 x 49 =

f) 15 x 99 =

6 Try splitting one or both of these numbers up to make the multiplication easier. Such as …

a) 35 x 18 = 35 x 2 x 9 = 70 x 9 =

b) 45 x 18 =

c) 28 x 15 =

d) 25 x 14 =

7 Use the answer to a) to help you with b) and c)

a) $\frac{1}{3}$ of 330 =

b) $\frac{1}{6}$ of 330 =

c) $\frac{1}{12}$ of 330 =

8 A farmer keeps cows and chickens. If there are 81 heads and 252 legs, how many cows and chickens are there?

Cows

Chickens

Multiplying - Written Methods

1 **a)** A supermarket sold 317 packs of yoghurt in one day. If there are 6 yoghurts in each pack, how many yoghurts were sold?

Yummy Yoghurts
6 pack

....

b) 124 packs of fromage frais were also sold. There are 12 pots of fromage frais in a pack. How many pots were sold altogether?

fromage Frais
12 pack

....

2 Paper clips are sold in boxes which contain 144 paper clips each.

a) How many paper clips are there in 12 boxes?

....

b) How many paper clips are there in 35 boxes?

....

3 Imran uses these number cards to make this multiplication:

3   4   5   6   7

5   3   7   **X**   4   6

a) What is the answer to Imran's multiplication?

....

b) If Imran changed the cards around, what would the largest possible answer be?

....

4 Fill in the missing digits:

a)
```
    ☐ 2
  X     7
  ───────
    4 3 ☐
  ───────
```

b)
```
  ☐ 7 ☐
  X     8
  ───────
  2 1 8 4
  ───────
```

c)
```
  ☐ 2 3
  X     6
  ───────
  2 5 3 ☐
  ───────
```

d)
```
    7 ☐ ☐
  X       8
  ─────────
  6 0 4 8
  ─────────
```

e)
```
      2 1 3
  X       1 4
  ───────────
  ☐ 1 ☐ 0
  ───────────
    ☐ 5 ☐
  ───────────
    2 9 8 2
  ───────────
```

f)
```
    ☐ 2 4
  X     2 5
  ─────────
  8 ☐ ☐ 0
  2 ☐ ☐ 0
  ─────────
  1 0 ☐ ☐ 0
  ─────────
```

Dividing - Written Methods

YOU MUST NOT USE A CALCULATOR

1 Calculate 456 ÷ 8.

....

2 A bag of 245 sweets is shared between 7 children. How many sweets do they get each?

....

3 Calculate 598 ÷ 13.

....

4 18 people share a prize of £486 equally between them. How much do they get each?

....

5 Alicia is planning to cycle 854 miles. She wants to split the journey into 14 equal days. How far does she need to cycle each day?

.... miles

6 1368 ball bearings are divided into boxes of 24. How many boxes will there be?

BEARINGS R'US
24 in a box

.... boxes

7 Put a ring around the correct answer to 546 ÷ 26.

26   16   21   31   22   32

Multiplying and Dividing Decimals

1 Calculate:

a) 4.15 x 6

b) 2.34 x 12

2 Make sure you have a rough idea of the answer before doing these.

a) 68.4 ÷ 6

b) 35.25 ÷ 15

3 If the "average family" has 2.4 children, how many children are there in …

a) 8 "average families"?

b) 35 "average families"?

4 Find the missing number.

a) 8 x ⬜ = 288

b) ⬜ x 21 = 462

c) 315 ÷ ⬜ = 63

d) 572 ÷ ⬜ = 22

e) ⬜ ÷ 28 = 35

f) ⬜ ÷ 15 = 261

5 Fill in the missing digits:

a) 7.⬜
4) 2 ⬜ .2

b) .⬜4
16) 3. 8 ⬜

c) ⬜ 7 ⬜ ÷ 1.2 = 23

Dividing - Remainders

(1) Work out 653 ÷ 17.

.... rem. ....

(2) 15 children share a bag of 576 sweets equally between them. How many sweets do they each get, and how many are left in the bag?

....

(3) Work these out giving the remainder as a fraction.

a) 95 ÷ 7

....

b) 47 ÷ 9

....

(4) Work these out using a decimal in the answer.

a) 141 ÷ 6

....

b) 329 ÷ 14

....

(5) 264 children are going on a trip to the zoo. There needs to be at least 1 adult for every 15 children. How many adults need to go with the children?

....

(6) Milk crates hold 24 bottles of milk each. A milkman needs to deliver 882 bottles of milk. How many crates of milk does he need?

....

Calculations - Negative Numbers

1 Here are the midday temperatures in five cities on the same day in February.

London	1°C
Moscow	-17°C
Paris	-2°C
Oslo	-8°C
Cairo	27°C

a) Which city had the coldest temperature?

b) What is the difference between the temperature in London and Moscow?

c) What is the difference between the temperature in Paris and Oslo?

d) The temperature in Oslo had gone down by 5°C at midnight. What was the midnight temperature in Oslo?

2 **a)** Circle two numbers with a difference of 10.

-6   -5   -4   -3   -2   -1

0   1   2   3   4   5

b) Circle two numbers which add up to 12.

12   -4   7   16   -1   -5

3 Look at these number cards.

| 3 | 5 | 11 | 15 | 9 |

a) Choose a card to give the answer -4.

$5 - \boxed{} = -4$

b) Choose a card to give the answer -2.

$-11 + \boxed{} = -2$

c) Choose three different cards to give the answer -1.

$\boxed{} - \boxed{} + \boxed{} = -1$

4 Use "+" or "−" signs to make these calculations correct.

a) $3 \boxed{} 7 = -4$

b) $-8 \boxed{} 12 = 4$

c) $3 \boxed{} 12 \boxed{} 2 = -7$

d) $14 \boxed{} 8 \boxed{} 19 = -13$

e) $-5 \boxed{} 17 \boxed{} 24 = -12$

f) $-18 \boxed{} 16 \boxed{} 12 = -22$

g) $-20 \boxed{} 13 \boxed{} 25 = -8$

h) $16 \boxed{} 6 \boxed{} 15 = 7$

i) $23 \boxed{} 4 \boxed{} 11 = 30$

Multiples and Factors

1 Here is a list of numbers:

2   5   9   13   4   27

a) Which of these numbers are multiples of 3?

b) Which of these numbers are factors of 12?

2 Write down all the factors of 28.

3 **a)** Write down the first five multiples of 7.

b) Which of these numbers are also factors of 63?

4 **a)** Circle the numbers below that are multiples of 3.

27   56   69   78   115   243

b) Circle the numbers below that are multiples of 6.

45   82   96   234   324   516

5 Circle the numbers below that are multiples of 2, 5 and 10.

12   15   25   50   90   145

6 Which of these numbers are divisible by 5?

310   135   252   815   553

7 **a)** Write down the first 8 multiples of 5.

b) Write down the first 8 multiples of 4.

c) What is the lowest common multiple of 4 and 5?

8 Michelle says:

8 x 6 = 48. So 48 is the lowest common multiple of 6 and 8.

Is Michelle correct? Explain you answer.

Square Numbers and Prime Numbers

1 Lottery balls are numbered from 1 to 49.

(1) (2) (3) (4) (5) (6) (7) (8) (9) (10) (11) (12) (13) (14) (15) (16) (17) (18) (19)
(20) (21) (22) (23) (24) (25) (26) (27) (28) (29) (30) (31) (32) (33) (34) (35) (36) (37) (38)
(39) (40) (41) (42) (43) (44) (45) (46) (47) (48) (49)

a) Which of these balls have square numbers on them?

b) Which of these balls have prime numbers on them?

2 A number multiplied by itself gives the answer 36. Circle the number.

1   2   3   4   5

6   7   8   9

3 I think of a number.

a) It is less than 20.
It is not a prime number.
It is an odd number.
It is not a factor of 30.
It is a multiple of 3.
What number am I thinking of?

b) It is less than 20.
It is a prime number.
It is a factor of 52.
It is an odd number.
What number am I thinking of?

4 Kiran thinks that 39 is a prime number. Explain why Kiran is wrong.

5 Find the prime factors of …

a) 60

b) 105

Number Patterns

1 Write down the next number in these patterns.

a) 2, 5, 8, 11, 14 ☐

b) 2, 6, 18, 54 ☐

c) 18, 13, 9, 6, 4 ☐

2 Here is a number pattern.
1, 4, 7, 10

The rule for continuing this pattern is "Add 3 each time." Write down the rule for each of these patterns.

a) 2, 4, 6, 8, 10, 12 ☐

b) 2, 4, 8, 16, 32, 64 ☐

c) 2, 4, 7, 11, 16, 22 ☐

3 For each pattern below you are given the first terms and the rule for continuing the pattern. Write down the next three terms.

a) 1, 5, ☐ ☐ ☐   Add 4 each time

b) 1, 5, ☐ ☐ ☐   Multiply by 5 each time

c) 1, 5, 10, ☐ ☐ ☐   The difference gets 1 bigger each time

4 Abdul is trying to find the 25th term in this pattern:

6, 12, 18, 24, 30 … He notices that term 1 is 6, term 2 is 12, term 3 is 18.
So the rule is "multiply the term number by 6." The 25th term will be 25 x 6 = 150.

a) Find the 75th term. ☐

b) Here is another pattern: 8, 14, 20, 26, 32 …
By comparing this pattern with the first one,
write down the rule and find the 75th term.

Rule: ☐   75th term: ☐

Formulas

1 Nisha is making shapes out of black tiles.

 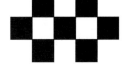 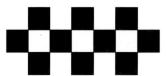 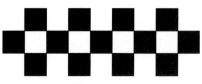

Shape 1   Shape 2   Shape 3   Shape 4

Shape Number	1	2	3	4
Number of black tiles	4	7	10	13

a) How many black tiles will Nisha need for shape 5?

[ ]

b) Nisha finds this formula for each shape: Number of Black Tiles = 3 x Shape number + 1.

Use Nisha's formula to find the number of black tiles she will need for:

i) Shape 6   [ ]

ii) Shape 9   [ ]

iii) Shape 20   [ ]

2 Joe uses his tiles to make these shapes:

Shape 1   Shape 2   Shape 3   Shape 4

Shape Number (n)	1	2	3	4
Number of black tiles (t)	5	8	11	14

Joe writes his formula using letters: t = 3n + 2.

Use Joe's formula to find how many black tiles he will need for:

a) Shape 5   [ ]

b) Shape 20   [ ]

c) Shape 50   [ ]

3 Rewrite these formulas using the letters in brackets.

a) Number of tiles (t) = 4 x Shape number (n) - 2   [ ]

b) Number of tiles (t) = 3 + Shape number (n) x 5   [ ]

Fractions

1 Shade in ¼ of this diagram.

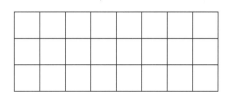

2 Draw a line joining any two shapes that have the same fraction shaded in.

A

B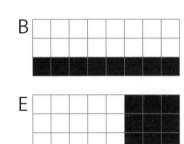

C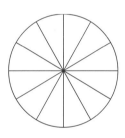

D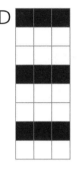

E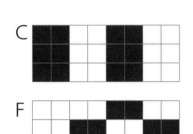

F

3 **a)** Shade in ¾ of this circle.

b) Shade in ⅔ of this circle.

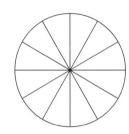

c) Which fraction is bigger ¾ or ⅔?

....

4 **a)** Draw <u>one</u> line to join two fractions which have the same value.

$\frac{2}{3}$

$\frac{3}{4}$

$\frac{4}{5}$

$\frac{5}{7}$

$\frac{6}{8}$

$\frac{1}{2}$

b) Explain how you know.

....
....

Simplifying Fractions

1 Place these dominoes in the spaces so that each fraction joins up with an equivalent fraction.

| $\frac{5}{6}$ | $\frac{9}{12}$ | | $\frac{10}{12}$ | $\frac{2}{3}$ |

| $\frac{8}{12}$ | $\frac{1}{4}$ | | $\frac{3}{4}$ | $\frac{2}{8}$ |

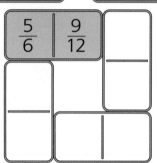

2 Write each of these fractions in its simplest form

a) $\frac{8}{10} =$

b) $\frac{6}{12} =$

c) $\frac{10}{15} =$

d) $\frac{18}{27} =$

3 Match the mixed numbers with the improper fractions on these dominoes.

| $3\frac{1}{4}$ | $\frac{9}{2}$ | | $\frac{3}{2}$ | $2\frac{3}{4}$ |

| $\frac{13}{4}$ | $1\frac{1}{2}$ | | $4\frac{1}{2}$ | $\frac{11}{4}$ |

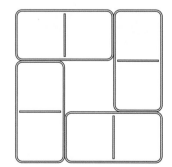

4 Write these improper fractions as mixed numbers.

a) $\frac{13}{4} =$

b) $\frac{12}{5} =$

c) $\frac{18}{10} =$

d) $\frac{20}{8} =$

5 Write these mixed numbers as improper fractions.

a) $2\frac{1}{4} =$

b) $3\frac{1}{3} =$

c) $2\frac{4}{5} =$

d) $1\frac{4}{7} =$

6 a) Mark the positions of these fractions on the number line. The first one has been done for you.

$\frac{1}{2}$ $\frac{2}{5}$ $\frac{1}{3}$ $\frac{1}{4}$ $\frac{7}{10}$

0   $\frac{1}{2}$ 1

b) Which fraction is the smallest?

7 Which fraction is the largest?

a) $\frac{3}{10}$ or $\frac{1}{4}$

b) $\frac{11}{8}$ or $\frac{4}{3}$

c) $2\frac{3}{4}$ or $\frac{18}{7}$

8 What number is halfway between

a) $\frac{3}{4}$ and 1 ?

b) $2\frac{1}{4}$ and $2\frac{1}{2}$?

Revision Guide Reference: Page 25

Percentages

1 Write in the missing numbers:

a) $\dfrac{1}{\Box} = 50\%$

b) $\dfrac{1}{4} = \boxed{}\,\%$

c) $\dfrac{\Box}{10} = 30\%$

d) $\dfrac{4}{\Box} = 80\%$

e) $\dfrac{8}{10} = \boxed{}\,\%$

f) $\dfrac{\Box}{\Box} = 75\%$

2 **a)** Shade $\dfrac{3}{5}$ of the shape below:

b) What percentage of the shape have you shaded?

.... %

3 Hayley went shopping in the sales for a coat.

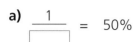

SALE $\frac{1}{3}$ OFF   SALE 35% OFF   SALE $\frac{3}{8}$ OFF

Coat A   Coat B   Coat C

a) Write $\dfrac{1}{3}$ as a percentage.   .... %

b) Write $\dfrac{3}{8}$ as a percentage.   .... %

c) Which coat has the biggest reduction?

....

4 Laura got $\dfrac{27}{40}$ in a maths test. Oliver got $\dfrac{35}{50}$ in a different maths test. Write each of these marks as a percentage and say who got the best mark.

Laura .... %   Oliver .... %

Best mark ....

5 Which of the following is the biggest? Use a number line to help you. Circle the correct answer.

a) 0.6, $\dfrac{7}{10}$, 65%   0 ⊢┬┬┬┬┬┬┬┬┬┐ 1

b) 0.3, $\dfrac{32}{100}$, 33%   0 ⊢┬┬┬┬┬┬┬┬┬┐ 1

Finding a Fraction and a Percentage of an Amount

1 Calculate the following.

a) $\frac{1}{4}$ of 36p =

b) $\frac{2}{5}$ of 30p =

c) 10% of £30 =

d) 35% of 80m =

2 The supermarket had two different boxes of cereal on special offer.

a) How many grams extra do you get if you buy the Corn Flakes?

_____ g

b) How many grams extra do you get if you buy the Corn Crispies?

_____ g

3 **a)** Calculate 24% of £325

b) Calculate 62% of £525.

4 Fill in the missing numbers.

a) $\frac{1}{2}$ of [ ] = 12

b) $\frac{1}{4}$ of [ ] = 45

c) $\frac{2}{3}$ of [ ] = 18

d) 10% of [ ] = 27

e) 40% of [ ] = 24

f) 75% of [ ] = 36

5 Tom is 160cm tall, Harry is 80% of Tom's height and Mick's height is half way between Tom's and Harry's. How tall is Mick?

_____ cm

Revision Guide Reference: Page 27

Proportions and Ratios

1 Here is a pattern of bricks.

a) How many black bricks to white bricks are there?

b) What fraction of the bricks are white?

2 Here is a traffic jam.

a) How many cars to vans are there?

b) What proportion of the vehicles are cars?

c) What proportion of the vehicles are yellow?

3 In a class of 30 children there are 2 boys for every 3 girls. How many girls are there?

4 In a bag of 60 sweets, 1 sweet in every 5 is a caramel. How many of the sweets are caramels?

5 A builder uses a mixture of 3 shovels of sand for every shovel of cement. His mixer can hold a total of 20 shovels. How many shovels of sand should he put in?

6 At the school disco there was one teacher for every 15 pupils. If there were 5 teachers, how many pupils were there?

7 If there are 8 lionesses for every male in a lion pack, and there are 4 males, how many lions are there altogether in a pack?

8 A glass of diluted squash is made up of 9 parts water to 1 part squash. What percentage of squash does it contain?

Solving Problems

1 Mrs. Roberts buys 9 drinks at 47p each and 6 drinks at 56p each. What is the total cost of the 15 drinks?

£ ....

2 **a)** A garden centre sells plants at £1.15 each. Find the cost of 25 plants.

£ ....

b) The garden centre also sells shrubs at £7 each. How many shrubs can be bought for £50?

....

3 A restaurant can seat up to 6 people around one table. How many tables are needed to seat 100 people?

....

4 Abid buys one Dando, one Try and one Footy. He pays with a £1 coin. How much change will he get?

DANDO 24p BANTIE 28p TRY!! 33p FOOTY 29p

.... p

5 A machine makes 80000 drawing pins every day. How many boxes can be filled?

150 Drawing Pins

....

6 Tennis balls cost 45p each. Shuttlecocks cost 35p each. John wants to buy both tennis balls and shuttlecocks. He spends £6.20 exactly. If he buys 6 tennis balls how many shuttlecocks does he buy?

....

Estimating and Rounding

1 Estimate the position of each arrow on these lines.

a) 0 ↑ 1000

b) 0 ↑ 10000

c) -20 ↑ 0

d) 0 ↑ 1

2 Estimate:

a) The number of crisps in a 30g bag.

b) The number of letters on this page.

c) The number of passengers on a full double-decker bus.

d) The number of bricks in a wall 10m long and 5m high.

e) The number of bars of chocolate you will eat in your lifetime.

≡149

3 What is:

a) 3 658 to the nearest 10?

b) 13 241 to the nearest 100?

c) 18 702 to the nearest 1000?

d) 2.5417 to one decimal place?

e) 2.5417 to the nearest whole number?

4 Mari said that the attendance at a pop festival was 43 000 to the nearest 1000. Isla said that there were 43 500 people to the nearest 100.

a) What could have been the exact attendance?

b) What could have been the lowest exact attendance?

Co-ordinates

1 Point A has co-ordinates (4, 7).
Write down the co-ordinates of the other points.

Point B (_____ , _____)

Point C (_____ , _____)

Point D (_____ , _____)

2 Plot these points on the grid, joining them up as you go along.

(2, 2) (0, 2) (-2, 0) (-2, -2) (0, -4)

(2, -4) (4, -2) (4, 0) (2, 2)

3 The crosses on the line are equally spaced.

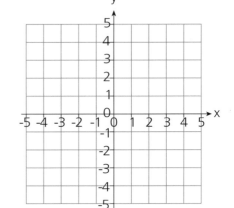

a) What are the co-ordinates of point A?

(_____ , _____)

b) What are the co-ordinates of point B?

(_____ , _____)

c) If the line was made longer, would the point with co-ordinates (10, 15) be on the line? Explain your answer.

_____

_____

4 Fill in the missing co-ordinates.

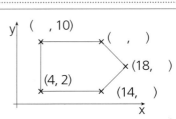

Describing Shapes

1 Here are some shapes:

a) Which shape has only one pair of parallel sides and is a quadrilateral?

b) What sort of polygon is shape E?

c) Which shape is not a polygon?

d) Which shape has the most pairs of parallel sides?

2 Here are 8 polygons:

a) Which of these polygons are quadrilaterals?

b) What sort of polygon is shape H?

c) Which of these polygons are pentagons?

d) Which of these polygons are hexagons?

e) Which of these polygons are octagons?

3 On the grid below, draw:

a) A hexagon with only one pair of parallel sides.

b) A regular quadrilateral.

Triangles and Quadrilaterals

1 Here are some triangles:

A B C D E

a) Which triangle is an equilateral triangle?

....

b) Which two triangles are isosceles triangles?

....

c) What makes the equilateral triangle different from the other triangles?

....

....

2 Draw and name a quadrilateral which has the following properties.

a) All sides are the same length, opposite sides are parallel, angles are not 90°.

b) Two pairs of touching sides are the same length. The diagonals meet at right angles. Opposite sides are not parallel.

c) The diagonals bisect each other, but are different lengths. The diagonals do not meet at right angles. Angles are not right angles.

3 What shape is a regular quadrilateral?

....

4 Andrew has some shape cards.

Square   Rectangle   Parallelogram   Rhombus   Trapezium

Place the cards in the sorting tree below.

Are all sides the same length?

YES → Are all the angles right angles? → YES → ....

NO → ....

NO → Are all the angles right angles? → YES → ....

NO → Are both pairs of opposite sides parallel? → YES → ....

NO → ....

Revision Guide Reference: Page 33

3-Dimensional Shapes

1 Rachel has the following solids.

A   B   C   D   E

Which solid fits the following description?

a) Solid ☐ has three faces, one is curved and the other two are circles.

b) Solid ☐ has five corners (vertices) and one square face

c) Solid ☐ has one curved face and one circular face.

d) Solid ☐ has twelve edges that are all the same length.

e) Solid ☐ has six faces, two are trapeziums, the other four are ....

(fill in the missing word)

2 What shape am I thinking of?

a) This shape has 4 faces. It is a polygon. Each face is an equilateral triangle.

....

b) This shape is not a polyhedron. It is a prism. Two of its faces are circles.

....

c) This shape has 12 edges. It is a polyhedron. Each face is a triangle.

....

3 Huw is looking at some 3-D shapes to see if they have any parallel faces and if they have any perpendicular faces. He is looking at:

Complete the table using a ✓ or a ✗. The first one has been done for you.

Cube

Cone

Dodecahedron

Cuboid

Sphere

	Some parallel faces	Some perpendicular faces
Cube	✓	✓
Cuboid		
Sphere		
Cone		
Dodecahedron		

4 Describe this shape in words. Give as much information as you can.

....

....

....

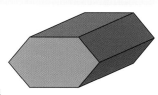

Angles

1 Choose the correct word from the list to make the sentences correct.

| Right | Isosceles | Acute | Radius |
| Reflex | Obtuse | Degree |

a) An angle that is between 90° and 180° is called an ☐☐☐☐ angle.

b) An angle that is less than 90° is called an ☐☐☐☐ angle.

c) A 90° angle is called a ☐☐☐☐ angle.

d) An angle that is between 180° and 360° is called a ☐☐☐☐ angle.

2 This pointer starts at 0 and turns in a clockwise direction

a) What number does it point to after a turn of 90°? ☐☐☐☐

b) What angle does it turn going from 0 to 2? ☐☐☐☐

c) What number does it point to after a turn of 225°? ☐☐☐☐

3 Here are some shapes …

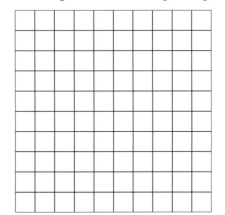

a) Which shapes have two acute and two obtuse angles? ☐☐☐☐

b) Which shapes have two right angles? ☐☐☐☐

c) Which shapes have not got any acute angles? ☐☐☐☐

4 Use the grid below to draw:

a) A pentagon with three right angles.

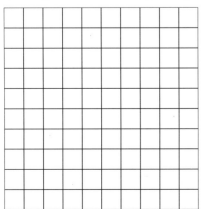

b) A hexagon with three right angles.

Measuring and Drawing Angles

1   Measure all the angles in each shape.

a)

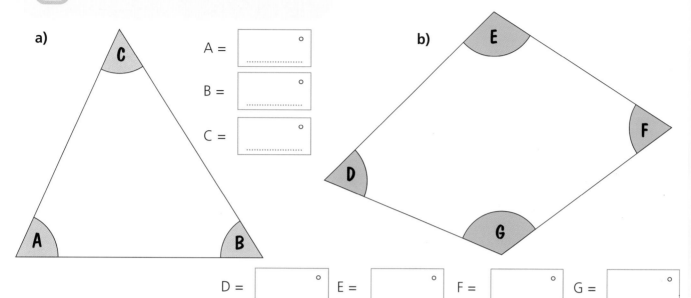

A = [____]°

B = [____]°

C = [____]°

b)

D = [____]°   E = [____]°   F = [____]°   G = [____]°

2   Here is a rough sketch of a kite.

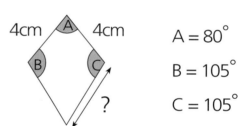

4cm   A   4cm

B   C

?

A = 80°

B = 105°

C = 105°

Make an accurate full size drawing of the kite and
measure the length of the side marked with a "?".
The first line has been drawn for you.

side marked? = [____] cm

Calculating Angles

1 Fill in the blanks in these sentences

a) The angles at a point add up to

b) The angles on a straight line add up to

c) The angles in a triangle add up to

2 Calculate the size of the missing angles.

a)
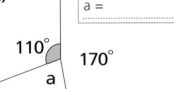
a =

110°   170°
a

b)
b =

30°
b

c)
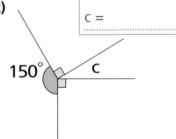
c =

150°   c

d)
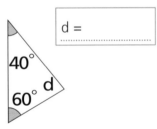
d =

40°
60° d

e)
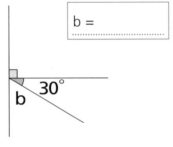
e =

72°
e

f)
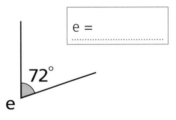
f =

52°
63°   f

3 **a)** Calculate the size of the angle x at the top of the child's swing.

x =

b) What sort of triangle is this?

x
70° 70°

4 Find the size of the missing angles in this bike frame.

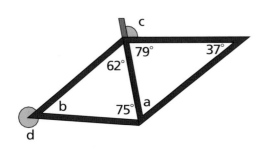

c
79°   37°
62°
b   75° a
d

a =

b =

c =

d =

Line Symmetry and Reflection

1 Year 6 have made some designs for a new school badge. For each badge draw a dotted line to show each line of symmetry.

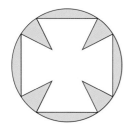  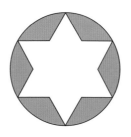 

2 Shade in two more squares so that the dotted line is a line of symmetry.

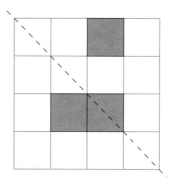

3 Draw the reflection of each shape in the mirror lines.

a)

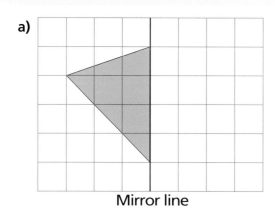

Mirror line

b)

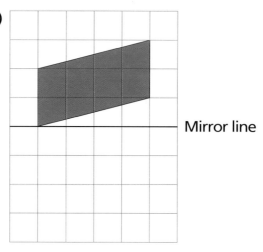

Mirror line

c)

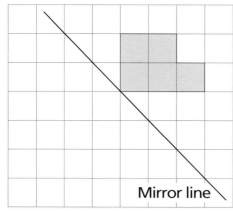

Mirror line

d)

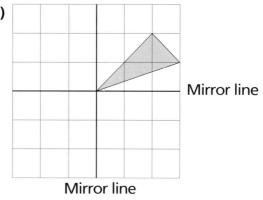

Mirror line

Translations and Rotations

1 Choose the correct type of transformation from REFLECTION, TRANSLATION, ROTATION and write it in the box to make these sentences correct:

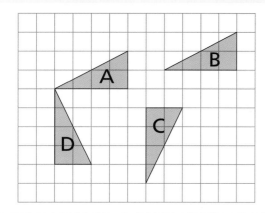

a) Triangle B is a [_____] of triangle A.

b) Triangle C is a [_____] of triangle A.

c) Triangle D is a [_____] of triangle A.

2 **a)** Translate this rectangle four places right and three places up.

b) Translate this shape three places left and two places up.

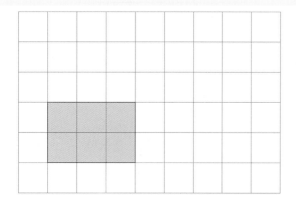

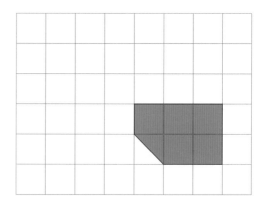

3 **a)** Turn this shape through one right angle in a clockwise direction around point C. Draw its new position.

b) Rotate this shape 90° in an anti-clockwise direction about point D. Draw its new position.

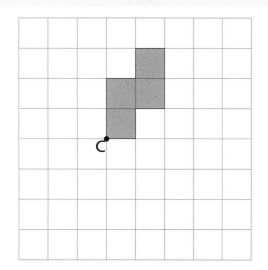

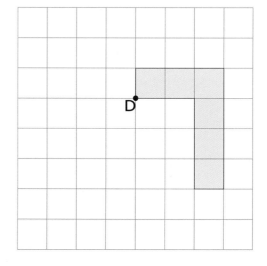

Congruent Shapes

1 Fill in the missing words:

Two shapes are congruent if they are exactly the

same .... and ....

2 Which two shapes below are congruent?

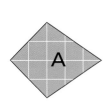
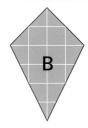

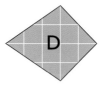
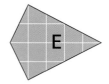

Shapes .... and .... are congruent

3 Which one of the shapes below has been cut out of the piece of cardboard? ....

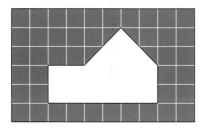

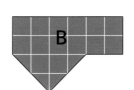

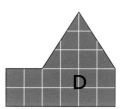

4 This shape is called an "arrowhead." Add six more "arrowheads" to the pattern below.

Making 3-D Models

1 Which of these nets DO NOT make a cube?

[   ] do not make a cube.

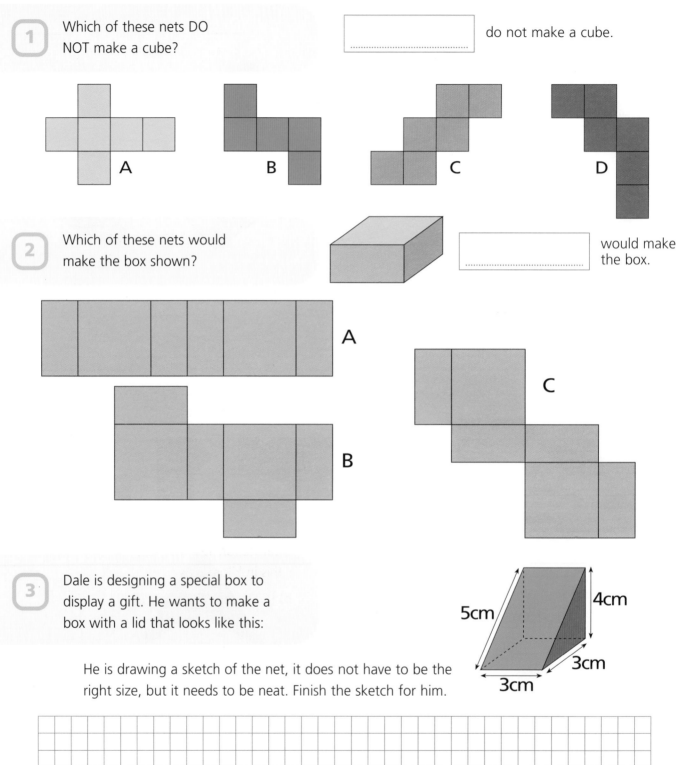

A   B   C   D

2 Which of these nets would make the box shown?

[   ] would make the box.

A

B

C

3 Dale is designing a special box to display a gift. He wants to make a box with a lid that looks like this:

He is drawing a sketch of the net, it does not have to be the right size, but it needs to be neat. Finish the sketch for him.

5cm

4cm

3cm

3cm

5cm

3cm

Revision Guide Reference: Page 41

Length

① Measure the length of each side of these triangles. Give your answer as accurately as you can.

a) Give your answers in centimetres.

.... cm

.... cm

.... cm

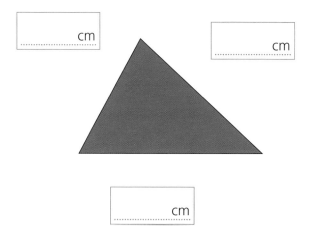

b) Give your answers in millimetres.

.... mm

.... mm

.... mm

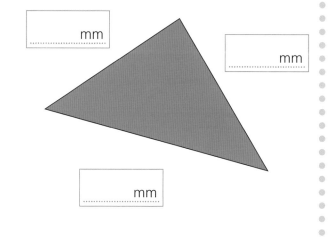

② Grace had her height measured when she was 18 months old. How tall is Grace?

.... cm

90cm

80cm

③ In a high jump competition ...

a) Mario jumped 1.15m, how many centimetres is this?

.... cm

b) Huw jumped 1.1m, how many centimetres is this?

.... cm

c) Wally jumped 0.97m, how many centimetres is this?

.... cm

④ James, Lynda and Bruce had a competition to see how far they could run in ten minutes.

a) James ran 1230m, how far is this in kilometres?

.... km

b) Lynda ran 1.36km, how far is this in metres?

.... m

c) Bruce ran 1600m, how far is this in kilometres?

.... km

⑤ In a cricket ball throwing competition, flags were placed where the balls landed, and then a tape measure was used to measure the distance thrown. Write down how far each ball was thrown.

A = ... m   B = ... m

C = ... m   D = ... m

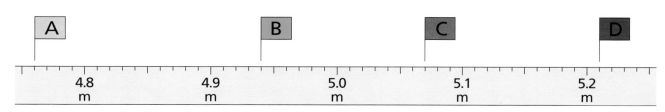

| A | B | C | D |

| 4.8 m | 4.9 m | 5.0 m | 5.1 m | 5.2 m |

Mass

1 Coal is sold in 50kg sacks. A lorry has 48 sacks of coal on it.

a) What is the mass of forty eight 50kg sacks in kg?

 kg

b) How many tonnes is this?

 t

2 Maisy puts 5g of sugar in her cup of tea. She has five cups a day, seven days a week for fifty two weeks a year. So in one year she has 5 x 5 x 7 x 52 = 9100g of sugar in her tea.

How many kg is this?
 kg

3 A vet in a zoo measured the mass of three baby chimpanzees.

They were a) 1.3kg b) 1.18kg and c) 1.29kg. Write each of these in grams.

a)
 g

b)
 g

c)
 g

4 What mass do each of these scales show?

a)

b)

c)

d)

e)

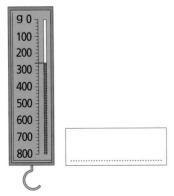

f)

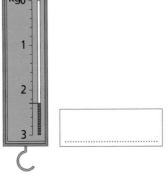

g)

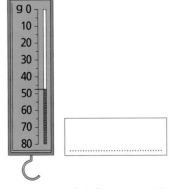

Capacity

1   A milk bottle holds 568ml of milk.

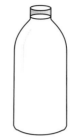

Write 568ml in litres.

```
                    l
```

2   A car engine has a capacity of 2.2 litres.

Write 2.2 litres in cm³.

```
                 cm³·
```

3   A tablespoon holds 25ml of sugar.

Write 25ml in cm³.

```
                 cm³·
```

4   How much water is in each of these containers?

a)   **b)**   **c)**   **d)**   **e)**

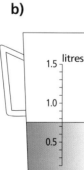  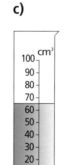  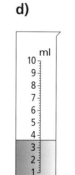

```
        ml              l              cm³·             ml              ml
```

5   Sabrina has to measure 700ml of milk in this jug. Draw a line to show where the milk should go up to.

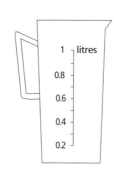

14

Time

1 **a)** How many seconds are there in:

i) 2 minutes? [ ] s **ii)** $3\frac{1}{2}$ minutes? [ ] s **iii)** $4\frac{3}{4}$ minutes? [ ] s

b) How many minutes are there in:

i) 3 hours? [ ] min **ii)** 150 seconds? [ ] min **iii)** $1\frac{1}{4}$ hours? [ ] min

c) How many hours are there in:

i) 420 min? [ ] hrs **ii)** 2 days? [ ] hrs **iii)** $2\frac{1}{2}$ days? [ ] hrs

2 Three friends are planning a sponsored bike ride.
They are hoping to cycle 400 miles in 96 hours.

a) How many days is 96 hours? [ ] days

b) How many miles a day on average is this? [ ] miles

3 How long is it from:

a) 8.30am to 11.40am? [ ] **b)** 11.45am to 1.05pm? [ ]

c) 9.30pm to 7.15am? [ ] **d)** 13.50 to 19.10? [ ]

4 **a)** The school day starts at 8.40am and finishes at 3.05pm. Write these times in 24 hour clock time:

Starts: [ ]

Finishes: [ ]

b) How long is the school day? [ ]

5 A television programme starts at 7.40 and lasts for 45 minutes. At what time does it finish? [ ]

6 A concert started at 8.30 and finished at 11.15. How long did the concert last for? [ ]

Shape, Space & Measures (15)

Imperial Units and Estimating Measures

1 Use the words "more" or "less" to complete the following statements.

a) 3m is a bit [＿＿] than 3 yards.

b) 8 yards is a bit [＿＿] than 8m.

c) 20lb is a bit [＿＿] than 10kg.

d) 1kg is a bit [＿＿] than 3lb.

e) 18 pints is a bit [＿＿] than 9 litres.

f) 12 litres is a bit [＿＿] than 24 pints.

2 Which is the bigger? Put a ring around your answer.

a) 3kg or 6lbs.　　**b)** 8kg or 4lbs.
c) 50lbs or 30kg.　**d)** 6 inches or 20cm.
e) 80cm or 80 inches.　**f)** 5cm or 10 inches.
g) 4m or 4 yards.　**h)** 1m or 80 inches.
i) 50cm or 1 yard.　**j)** 2 litres or 5 pints.
k) 8 pints or 16 litres.　**l)** 40 litres or 60 pints.

3 A cardboard box can safely hold up to 10kg without breaking. How many 1lb jars of jam can be safely carried in the box?

[＿＿] jars of jam

4 Donovan Bailey ran 100m in 9.84 seconds, setting a new world record. Estimate how long you think it would take him to run 100 yards. Explain your answer.

5 An adult is about 1.8m high.

a) Estimate the height of a classroom door. [＿＿] m

b) Estimate the height of a room in your house. [＿＿] m

c) Estimate the height of a house. [＿＿] m

d) A skyscraper has 52 floors. Estimate its height. [＿＿] m

6 4 large potatoes weigh about 1kg.

a) Estimate how many potatoes there will be in a 25kg sack. [＿＿]

b) 10 potatoes are in a bag, estimate their mass. [＿＿] kg

7 1 litre of lemonade weighs about 1kg. About 15 glasses can be poured from a 1 litre bottle. Estimate the capacity of each glass and the mass of lemonade in each glass.

Capacity = [＿＿]

Mass of lemonade = [＿＿]

Revision Guide Reference: Page 46　43

Perimeter

1 On the grid below draw a rectangle with a perimeter of …

a) 12cm

b) 10cm

2 Find the perimeter of each of these shapes.

a)

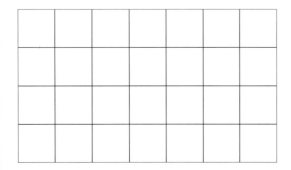

10cm 6cm
8cm

_____ cm

b)

5m
8m

_____ m

c)

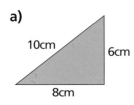

2cm
2cm
3cm
6cm

_____ cm

d)

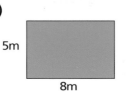

4m
11m
6m

_____ m

3 By measuring accurately find the perimeter of these shapes:

a)

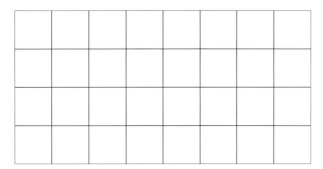

_____ cm

b)

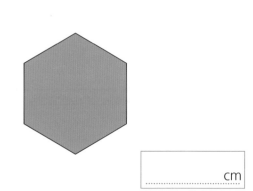

_____ cm

4 Rashid is making loops out of regular octagons. Each edge is 2cm. Find the length of the outer edge of each loop.

a)

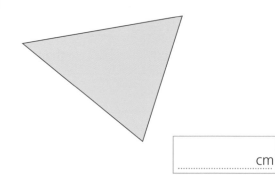

2cm
2cm

_____ cm

b)

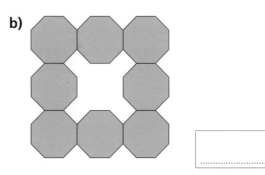

_____ cm

Revision Guide Reference: Page 47

Area

1 The area of each square on the grid is 1cm². What is the area of these shapes?

a)

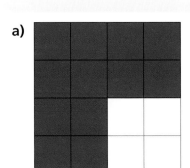

_____ cm²

b)

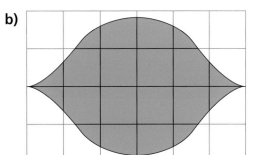

_____ cm²

2 **a)** On the grid below draw a rectangle with an area of 12cm².

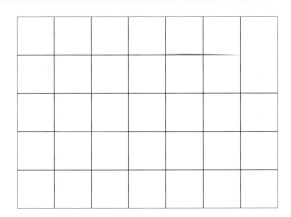

b) On the grid below draw a triangle with an area of 6cm².

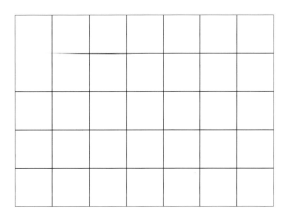

3 This square has an area of 1cm². So these triangles have an area of $\frac{1}{2}$ cm² each.

a) Four of these triangles make this square.

What is its area? _____ cm²

b) Draw a square with an area of 8cm² on this grid.

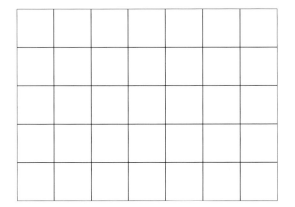

c) What is the area of this rectangle?

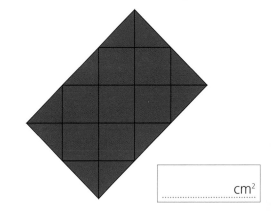

_____ cm²

More Area

1 Use the formula: Area = Length x Width, to find the area of these rectangles.

a)

3cm

6cm

.... cm²

b)

30cm

20cm

.... cm²

c)

4mm

17mm

.... mm²

2 By splitting these shapes into rectangles, calculate their areas.

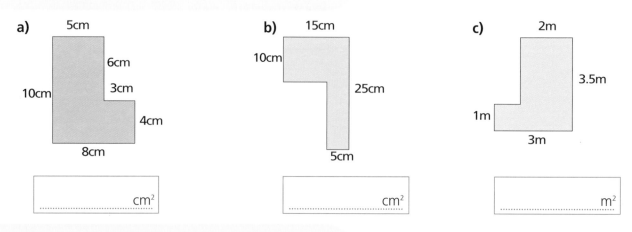

a)

5cm

6cm

3cm

10cm

4cm

8cm

.... cm²

b)

15cm

10cm

25cm

5cm

.... cm²

c)

2m

3.5m

1m

3m

.... m²

3 Calculate the area of these triangles.

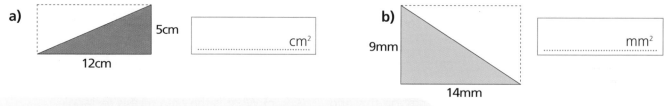

a)

5cm

12cm

.... cm²

b)

9mm

14mm

.... mm²

4 These shapes are drawn accurately. Calculate their area by using a ruler to measure any lengths that you may need.

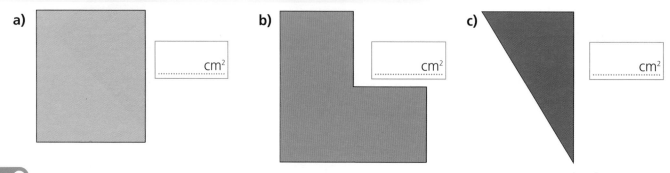

a)

.... cm²

b)

.... cm²

c)

.... cm²

Handling Data ❶

Collecting Data

1 Andrew did a survey of how the children in his class got to school. He collected this data in a tally chart.

a) Fill in the frequency column.

Method	Tally	Frequency
Walk	卌 卌 I	
Cycle	III	
Car	卌 卌 卌	
Bus	卌 I	
	TOTAL =	

b) What was the most common way of getting to school?

c) How many children are there in Andrew's class?

28	35	21	29	27	33	26	28	37	29
30	32	36	24	31	30	38	22	25	27
31	33	29	34	26	28	24	31	28	26
32	30	28	35	33	29	27	20	26	22

2 A greengrocer counted the number of grapes in 40 bunches. She recorded the number of grapes in each bunch in a list.

a) Put these amounts in the tally chart below.

Number of Grapes	Tally	Frequency
20 -24		
25 -29		
30 - 34		
35 - 39		
	TOTAL =	

b) How many bunches had between 25 and 34 grapes on them?

c) How many bunches had less than 30 grapes on them?

d) How many bunches had more than 25 grapes on them?

Bar Charts and Pictograms

1 Gary drew this bar chart to display the results of his survey on children's pets. Each bar shows the number of each type of pet.

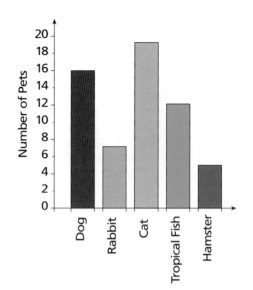

a) How many pets are dogs?

b) How many pets are cats?

c) Gary says that more people have tropical fish than rabbits. Could he be wrong? Explain your answer.

2 Michaela counted the number of chips people got with their dinners.

Number of chips	5 - 9	10 - 14	15 - 19	20 - 24
Number of people	3	18	22	7

Complete Michaela's bar chart for her.

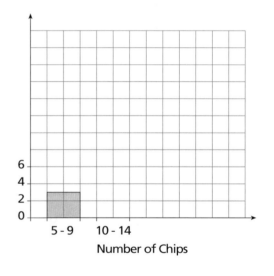

3 Salim displayed the results of his survey on people's pocket money in a pictogram.

Amount of pocket money	Number of People
£1.00 to £1.99	☺ ☺ ☺
£2.00 to £2.99	☺ ☺ ☺ ☺ ☾
£3.00 to £3.99	☺ ☺ ☺ ☺ ☺ ☾
£4.00 to £4.99	☺ ☾

Key: ☺ = 5 people

a) How many people get £1.00 to £1.99?

b) Estimate how many people get £2.00 to £2.99.

c) Estimate how many people get £4.00 to £4.99.

d) How many people did Salim carry out his survey on?

Revision Guide Reference: Page 51

Pie Charts and Sorting Diagrams

1 A newsagent works out how much money she gets from selling different items. She uses a pie chart to show this.

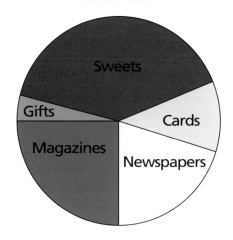

a) Estimate what fraction of her income is from cards.

b) If she gets a total of £800 a week, how much does she get from selling magazines?

c) Estimate how much money she gets from selling sweets.

d) Estimate how much money she gets from selling gifts.

2 Natalie has some number cards. Sort them using the Venn Diagram.

| 5 | 9 | 36 | 45 | 25 | 16 |

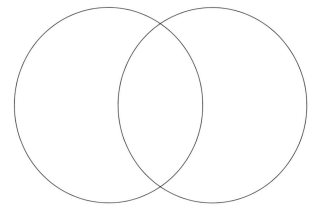

Odd numbers   Square numbers

3 Use the Carroll Diagram to sort these shapes.

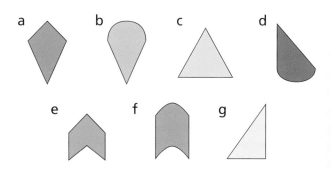

	Polygon	Not a Polygon
Symmetry		
No symmetry		

4 Draw a triangle in each of the three regions of the Venn Diagram below.

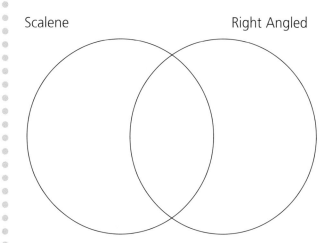

Scalene   Right Angled

Line Graphs and Types of Data

1 Miss Skinner, the science teacher, recorded the temperature in her classroom every hour from 8am to 5pm. She put the results on a line graph.

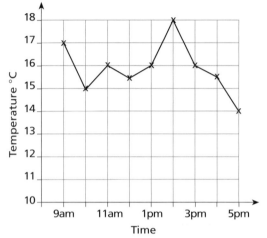

a) What was the highest temperature recorded?

b) What was the lowest temperature recorded?

c) Between which two times was there the greatest rise in recorded temperature?

2 Lee recorded his mass every month for six consecutive months. Draw a line graph to show Lee's results.

Month	Jan	Feb	Mar	Apr	May	Jun
Mass (kg)	50	51	53	51	49	48

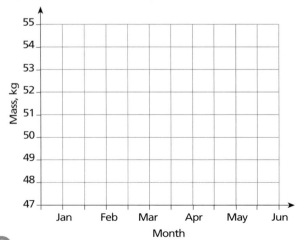

3 Say whether this data is discrete or continuous.

a) The number of pages in a book.

b) The amount of money spent at a supermarket.

c) The length of a piece of string.

d) The mass of an elephant.

e) The age of the children in a park.

4 Describe the difference between discrete data and continuous data.

Averages

① Kim has a job. She is asked to check that the mean (average) number of matches in a box is 48. She counts the number of matches in ten different boxes. This is what she found.

46 49 51 47 48 48 51 47 46 48

a) Calculate the mean number of matches.

_____ matches

b) What is the median number of matches?

_____ matches

c) What number of matches is the mode?

_____ matches

② In a mental arithmetic test a class got these marks.

24	22	11	15	21	23	22	16
20	18	17	19	18	16	21	24
19	20	23	21	17	20	15	20
21	22	20	18	19	12		

a) What is the range of these marks?

b) Calculate the mean mark.

c) What is the median test mark?

d) Which test mark is the mode?

③ Lucy is training for a swimming race. She swims ten lengths. These are her times for each length in seconds.

31.2   30.8   31.1   29.4   28.6
31.5   30.4   29.9   27.2   32.1

a) What is the range of these times?

b) What is the median time?

c) What is the mean time?

④ Find five numbers that have a range of 5, a median of 16 and a mean of 15.

⑤ The lowest night-time temperatures in a Scottish Village over two weeks were recorded in this table.

2   -3   -5   -1   0   2   4
3   1   0   -1   -2   2   5

a) What is the range of these temperatures?

b) What is the mean temperature?

6

Probability

1 Here is a probability scale.

Impossible		A		Certain

Show where you think each of these statements should be on the scale.
The first one has been done for you.
A "I am equally likely to get a head or tail when I toss a coin."
B "I think I will probably pass my maths exam."
C "It is unlikely to rain today."
D "It could possibly snow tomorrow."
E "There is quite a good chance of Michael winning his race."

2 Choose a word to describe the probability of these events happening.

a) The next dog you see being brown

b) The next cow you see being green

c) It raining in France in July

d) Winning the National Lottery

05 07 13 28 35 44

3 Emma threw a die 100 times and recorded the results. She got 33 sixes. Do you think it was a fair die? Give a reason.

4 Put these events in order from most likely to least likely.
Use a word to describe the probability of each event.

A You washing your hair in the next 48 hours.

B Tomorrow's school dinner being your favourite.

C You being poorly on your birthday.

D You getting a level 4 or 5 in your maths exam.

Most Likely➔

➔ Least Likely